THE POPE WHO
LOVES SOCCER

THE POPE WHO LOVES SOCCER

By

Michael Part

EDITOR: Y Ginsberg
RESEARCH: Diego Melamed
COVER DESIGN: Yosi Ohayon
FRONT COVER PICTURES: Youth picture, Reuters / Courtesy Bergoglio family / Handout
Pope Francis holding the ball, All image rights and copyrights reserved to the Photographic Service of L'Osservatore Romano.
BACK COVER PICTURES: All image rights and copyrights reserved to the Photographic Service of L'Osservatore Romano.
Page 32, 74, 78 pictures: Reuters / Courtesy of Maria Elena Bergoglio/Handout
Page 50, 122, 123 pictures: Reuters / San Lorenzo Soccer Club / Handout
Page 84 picture: AP Photo / Alessandra Tarantino
Page 100, 120 pictures: Reuters / L'Osservatore Romano
Page 122 picture: Reuters / Handout - Prensa San Lorenzo
Page 123 picture: Reuters / San Lorenzo soccer club/Handout

Page Layout Design: Lynn M. Snyder, Nosy Rosy Designs

Library of Congress
Cataloging-in-Publication data available.

ISBN: 978-1-938591-12-9

Published by Sole Books, Beverly Hills, California
Printed in the United States of America
First edition October 2013
10 9 8 7 6 5 4 3 2 1

www.solebooks.com

To My Mother and Father

Table of Contents

CHAPTER I

Two Arrivals

The passenger ship *Principessa Malfada*, two weeks out of Genoa, Italy, shudders and rocks as its starboard propeller shaft shatters in the dark waters off the coast of Brazil. The shaft breaks loose, swings around, and cuts huge gashes in the hull. A monster wave dwarfs the ship—and engulfs it...

Somewhere over the Atlantic, in the early morning hours, Cardinal Jorge Mario Bergoglio, the Archbishop of Buenos Aires,

slept in his seat on the wide body jet.
When the wheels of the plane screeched
down on the tarmac at Fiumicino Airport,
The Cardinal woke up. He had just landed
in Rome. He had been flying all night from
Buenos Aires, Argentina. The Roman
Catholic Church had summoned him to
Rome to form a Papal conclave with 115
other Cardinals from around the world in
order to elect a new Pope, who would become
the leader of the Catholic Church. When all
the Cardinals of the world come together,
they become the College of Cardinals. The
election of the new Pope is big news around
the world and the whole world watches
intently.

Two weeks earlier, Pope Benedict XVI,
Joseph Ratzinger, the current Pope and The
Cardinal's friend, had unexpectedly resigned.
He felt he no longer had the strength because
of his advanced age to fulfill his duties. This
was the first time a Pope had resigned since

Pope Gregory XII resigned in 1415.

The Cardinal checked his watch. It was March 3, 2013, 9:30 am. This was the latest he had slept in a long time. He usually woke up punctually at 4:30 am. For him, 9:30 in the morning was the middle of the day. He stretched out his legs and his feet banged into the seat in front of him. When the Church called him to Rome, they offered him a fancier Business Class seat, but he turned it down. "Donate the excess to the poor," he instructed them. "They need it more than I need a fancy seat." He never traveled in the trappings of a Cardinal and wore the black vestments of a priest.

Rome in March was still chilly. The Cardinal put on a dark overcoat. He could hardly wait to get to the city and walk among the people. His parents, Mario and Regina, were from Northern Italy and he learned to speak the language fluently as a boy, thanks to his Grandma Rosa. She used the story of the incidents concerning his birth, to give him a healthy dose of the old country language.

* * * *

Rosa Bergoglio paced in front of her husband, Giovanni, and her son, Mario, who were both sitting on a divan in the living room of their fourth floor family home in Buenos Aires. It was December 17, 1936. Mario leaped nervously to his feet when he heard his wife, Regina, screaming. "Is she dying?!" he asked.

His mother, Rosa, pushed him back down. "No, Mario. She is giving birth. Give her a chance."

Giovanni Bergoglio patted his son on the back. "This is what happens when a baby comes. And do not forget. With every baby comes a loaf of bread."

Mario nodded respectfully. "Were you scared when I was born, Papa?" he asked.

Rosa shot Giovanni a look and Giovanni

shrunk under her watchful eyes. "I was in the woods."

"He went for a walk," Rosa said. "He couldn't take the heat."

Mario laughed and Rosa gave her husband Giovanni a loving smile.

"Mama is right," Giovanni said. "I couldn't."

Then a baby cried in the other room and Rosa and Giovanni and Mario looked at each other. Rosa nodded and smiled. Still, no one said a word until the midwife came in carrying Mario's newborn son. The baby wailed, and his cries echoed off the walls of their home. "Congratulations! It's a boy!" she announced.

"Regina would like to call him Jorge Mario," the midwife said, delivering the baby to Mario's arms.

Mario took his newborn son, then looked at his mother and his father and said, "Is it too soon to take Jorge to his first San Lorenzo soccer game?"

Everyone laughed.

Two Continents

As The Cardinal waited in line at customs, he opened his black briefcase to make sure he had his two-volume Breviary of prayers, his appointment book, his wallet, and his return flight ticket. People believed that the new Pope would probably be either an Italian or an American. The Cardinal didn't expect to be elected Pope this time around. For him, it was over in 2005 when he came in second to his friend, Pope Benedict XVI. He expected to return home to

Buenos Aires in time for Holy Week. He had written a homily on the flight over and he could not wait to deliver it to his flock back home.

But there was an old saying his father, Mario, used to tell him and his other brothers and sisters when they were convinced they knew how things would turn out. He said it came from something the great Albert Einstein once said:

"Want to make God laugh? Make plans."

* * * *

Mario Bergoglio, The Cardinal's father, just 21 years old in 1927, bounced in the seat of his horse-drawn cart as he approached the shipping port in the Italian city of Genoa. When he reached the docks, he pulled the reins hard. "Ferma!" he shouted at the old horse and it happily came to an abrupt stop. It had been an all-day trip from his hilly commune in

Portacomaro, a hundred kilometers north.

Mario jumped down out of the cart. He hurried over to the Navigazione Generale Italiana Shipping Company building near the dock, yanked the hat off his head, and went inside.

Mario sat across from a booking agent who looked at him as if he were from Mars. Something did not feel right. The agent checked his papers. Looked at him again. Mario shifted uncomfortably in his seat. "I'm afraid all staterooms are booked for the Principessa Malfada," the booking agent finally said.

"But my family made reservations months ago," Mario argued, reaching into an inside pocket in his jacket and pulling out a folded piece of paper; unfolding it, he shoved it across the desk at the booking agent.

The booking agent picked up the piece of paper dispassionately, glanced at it quickly, and then shoved it back at Mario. "The rate for these passages, I see here, is too low," he said, poking it with his finger. "Someone made a mistake.

That cabin has been booked at a much higher rate. Next," the booking agent said, craning his head around Mario to look at the family standing in line behind him, letting them know it was their turn.

"Well, is there anything available in another class?" Mario asked, refusing to budge from his seat.

"I told you. The Principessa Malfada is sold out. In all classes," he said. "NEXT!"

Mario was depressed. He had dreamt of the day they would leave their village and travel to the new world. There, in Buenos Aires, his uncles were doing great. Here in Italy, things had turned ugly. It was hard for the Bergoglios to make ends meet. He could not see any future in the village of Portacomaro. And he could not see himself living under the fascist dictator, Mussolini, who ruled with an iron fist. He could not wait to get out.

But now, all his dreams were shattered.

*Two weeks later, Mario Jose Bergoglio raced
into the family home in Portacomaro. His
parents, Rosa and Giovanni, were setting the
supper table. Mario slapped the newspaper down
on the table for all to see. The headline was one
of the biggest they had ever seen and the size of
the type was usually reserved exclusively for the
ends of wars and assassinations. But this time,
it was for a shipwreck:*

PRINCIPESSA MALFADA SINKS!

*Rosa drifted into Giovanni's arms as all three
of them stared at the newspaper headline on the
table. No one said anything for a long time.
Finally, Rosa said, "It is a miracle."*

*Giovanni looked at his son and said, "Mama
is right."*

*It took the Bergoglio family two more years
before they could leave Italy and immigrate to
Argentina. They arrived in Buenos Aires, the
capital of Argentina, in February of 1929. Rosa*

Bergoglio, who despite the heat, was dressed elegantly in a long coat with fur collar, was the first of her family off the ship, the Giulio Cesare. She was followed by her husband, Giovanni, and their son, Mario. A porter felt sorry for Rosa and stepped up to her to help her with her bags. "Ma'am would you also like me to get your coat?" he asked, reaching for it. She pulled away from him. "No, señor, thank you. I am fine," she said in perfect Spanish. The porter shrugged, picked up her bags and started carrying them away. The Bergoglios followed the porters to a car that was waiting for them to take them home.

They marveled at their four-story family house, planted on the bustling street. Rosa hesitantly stepped into the elevator car at her son's urging, but had no idea what to do once she got in there. She had never seen an elevator, let alone been in one. Until now.

"Phew!" she said as she got off the elevator on the fourth floor. She immediately threw off her heavy coat and then did an odd thing. Instead *of hanging it up, she spread it out on the kitchen table. Mario and Giovanni and his brothers brought in all the luggage and stacked it in the living room, paying her no mind.*

Rosa grabbed a butcher knife from the knife block on the counter, and without hesitation, cut open the seam in the silk lining of the coat. Then she picked up the coat and shook it. As if by magic, thousands of Lira notes spilled out on the kitchen table. When she finished shaking the coat, she carelessly tossed it aside. "I thought I was going to die when I got off that ship," she said, giggling. "It was so hot!"

Giovanni and his three brothers and Mario all shared the laugh.

* * * *

The Cardinal remembered what their laughter sounded like from when he was a boy growing up in Buenos Aires. It was music to his ears. Now he was back in the Old World:

Rome. Rome was in the Old World and Buenos Aires was in the New World. And he felt at home in both worlds.

CHAPTER 3

Jersey Number 4

When Cardinal Bergoglio exited the airport terminal, his briefcase in one hand, his rollaway suitcase in the other, it was colder than he expected. He buttoned the last button on his dark overcoat and raised the collar to keep his neck warm. He spotted a fellow Cardinal and waved and the Cardinal waved back just before he entered the backseat of his black sedan and sped away. There were paparazzi everywhere waiting for cardinals who

came from all over the world, but Cardinal
Bergoglio, in his black priestly vestments,
drew no attention. They were after Cardinals,
not priests.

The Cardinal waited patiently at the
bus stop and when a city bus finally arrived,
he climbed aboard. His favorite mode of
transport was not a limousine, or even a
private sedan, but a city bus or subway. On
a bus, he could sit with people and talk to
them, be a part of their lives, listen to them,
comfort them, and perhaps help them.

The Cardinal chose a seat in the middle
of the bus. It was 45 minutes to Vatican
City, the smallest independent city-state
in the world, and the only city-state that
existed within another city. Vatican City was
founded in 1929, the same year the Bergoglio
family immigrated to Buenos Aires.

The Cardinal had a nickname for Vatican
City. He called it "work." He knew all about
work. When he finished primary school at age

13 and was ready for high school, his father informed him that was going to get a job over the summer break. Good to his word, Mario Bergoglio found his son a job in his railway office where he worked as an accountant. The Cardinal started out sweeping the floors, but by the fourth year, he was performing administrative duties. His father had given him the gift of a lifetime: a work ethic.

The bus radio blared news about the coming election of a new Pope, followed by an aria sung by one of his favorite opera stars. The Cardinal loved opera more than any other music and now he was in Italy, the country that gave birth to this great art form. The Cardinal closed his eyes and returned to Buenos Aires.

* * * *

Mario and Regina Bergoglio stared in wonder at their infant son, Jorge. An opera played softly from the radio, but it was drowned out by little Jorge's crying. Mario and Regina met at Mass one Sunday and after a decent courtship they married. They moved to this house on Membrillar Street, in the heart of the Flores district.

Mario looked at his crying son and shrugged. "I think he has potential. As an alto."

"Alto?" Regina laughed. "You call that melodic?"

"No, I would say it was more like — deafening!" Mario shot back and Regina laughed. She nodded at the radio across the room. "Mario, please turn it up."

Mario padded across the room in his stocking feet, turned the volume knob on the radio, and the soaring melodies of 'Madame Butterfly' instantly filled the room. State Radio was broadcasting a special presentation of the Puccini opera, one of their favorites, and just as Mario never missed a San Lorenzo soccer match on

Sunday, he and his wife never missed an opera on Saturday night. The Cardinal always thought his father gave in to his mother every Saturday night so he could go to a soccer match on Sunday. After mass, of course.

On the radio, the great soprano Mirella Freni began her magnificent aria.

And Jorge instantly stopped crying.

Mario and Regina looked at each other and laughed.

They always laughed when they told The Cardinal this story and they told it to him a lot over the years.

* * * *

The city of Rome came into view. The Cardinal always felt rejuvenated in Rome.

The bus made a sharp turn.

A group of boys wearing unmatched soccer jerseys played a pick-up game of soccer on the grassy expanse in the middle of a park, surrounded by speeding traffic.

One of the boys had a number 4 on his jersey. That was The Cardinal's number, when he played right back with his friends in his neighborhood square back home. The park was officially called Herminia Brumana Square, just down the street from his house on Membrillar Street in Buenos Aires. But to Jorge and his friends, it was the pitch.

* * * *

The school bell rang loudly at Municipal School No. 8 on Calle Varelo. The doors burst open, and students poured out of the room and down the stairs. Jorge pulled off his school shirt as he loped down the stairs, revealing his soccer jersey underneath. His friends, Ernesto Llach and Nestor Carbajo, were already waiting for him, shirts in hand, jerseys on. When Jorge joined them, the threesome charged across the school grounds towards the gate, and headed for the square.

Minutes later, Nestor shouted: "Jorgito!" He waved his arms around like a wild man. "Here!"

Jorge moved the ball from his left to his right and shot a pass across the makeshift field in Herminia Brumana Square straight to his best friend in the whole world, Nestor. Ernesto made a run and Nestor pretended to pass the ball to him, but decided to dribble onward, passing two defenders, and slammed the ball into the goal, which was just a park bench marking the goal posts.

That was how they did it back then: nothing fancy. No marked lines or goals. Everything was improvised. The beautiful game was not only beautiful because it was fun to play, it was beautiful because it was for all; it did not need expensive equipment or expensive space. Just a piece of land, a ball, and some kids with a passion for a match.

There was graffiti on one of the walls that said, 'los Cuervos de Boedo' — the Boedo Crows. Boedo was the name of the barrio, the neighborhood next door to Flores, where Jorge lived. They were nicknamed The Crows because the San Lorenzo de Almagro soccer team began on the church grounds by a priest named Lorenzo Massa. Since priests always dressed in black, they were called the Crows. Officially, their name was 'The Saints,' or 'The Cyclones,' but to those in the know, to those who truly loved them, to the diehard fans like the entire Bergoglio family, they were The Crows.

Every boy in Flores and Boedo believed in their hearts that the best soccer team in Argentina was the San Lorenzo de Almagro football club.

Nestor learned to love the Crows from his father, and Jorge learned from his father. It was like an inheritance. There were other teams in Buenos Aires, like Boca Junior, River Plate, and Independiente. But in Flores, there was only one team: the pride of Boedo, the San Lorenzo de Almagro Crows — 'Los Cuervos de Boedo.'

GOAL!!

Nestor scored another one. Jorge raised his arms in the air, charged across the pitch, and picked him up and hugged him victoriously. "Just like Pontoni, right?" Nestor shouted.

They were talking about Rene Pontoni, the greatest striker who ever lived, if you asked Jorgito or Nestor. And 1946 was the greatest year for Pontoni and his team. To Jorgito and Nestor, Pontoni was a living legend.

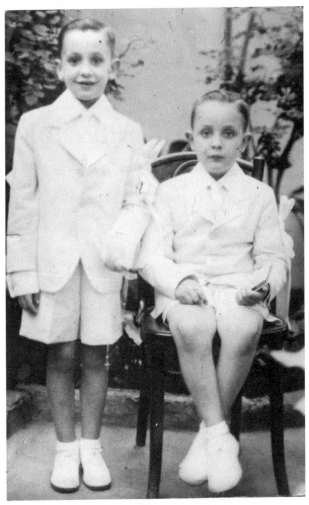

Brothers Jorge and Oscar

CHAPTER 4

The Most Amazing Year

Rene Alejandro Pontoni was born in Santa Fe, Argentina in 1920. He made his debut for the Argentina national team in 1942 as a striker and led his team to become the South American Champions in 1945, 1946, and 1947, scoring 19 goals in 19 games. In 1946 he was offered a contract with FC Barcelona, but unlike Diego Maradona and Leo Messi, two Argentinians who joined the club years later, Pontoni declined.

What was important to Jorge, Nestor, and Ernesto was what Pontoni did in 1944: he joined San Lorenzo. Pontoni was the quintessential Argentine hero in a country with a rich and great tradition of soccer.

The Bergoglio family did things like clockwork on the weekends: every Saturday they went to Grandma Rosa's house and listened to opera, and every Sunday they went to a soccer match.

Mario looked out at the local field, known as the Gasómetro, and watched the teams warm up. He held his wife Regina's hand and helped her to her seat, then sat down next to her. The children all plopped down into the surrounding seats. Jorge sat next to his father. They had arrived early and as a result, got seats on the 50-yard-line, just a few rows up. It was an important match: their beloved San Lorenzo Crows were about to battle it out against the formidable Racing de Avellaneda. Racing was a tough team and this late in the season, every game counted. The Crows had had a great run and were hoping to win the championship. But first they had to get past Racing.

It was October 20, 1946, the day when everyone in the Gasómetro stands went dead quiet. The Crows were killing Racing. They were already up 4-0, and the stands were electrified with excitement. Then Francisco de la Mata dribbled the ball across the field looking for the "Master"—Rene Pontoni, finally spotting him out of the corner of his eye.

Pontoni had his back to the goal.

Jorge stood up slowly and held his breath.

Yerba and Palma were all over Pontoni.

The crowd was on its feet.

De La Mata shot the ball and Pontoni took it on his chest and let it drop to his right foot where he took control of it for what seemed like a lifetime. He juggled it, never letting it hit the ground. Then without warning, he faked a run to the right, spun around and went hard left, beating out both his defenders to hammer the ball past Ricardo, the Racing goalkeeper.

The stadium went perfectly silent.

Not one of the 34,000 spectators said a word.

Three seconds of absolute silence in the Gasómetro.

Then the crowd erupted in wild cheering for the move that ended with a glorious goal by Pontoni!

At that time, there were no big screens in the stadium for the replay and no TV to watch the recorded game. The magic of the moment was simply recorded permanently in the heart of 10-year-old Jorge, and he would replay this goal in his mind often throughout the years.

After the game, when they relived the great moments, Jorge's father told him that it was a "Nobel Prize-winning goal."

Back in the square, the boys continued playing their daily pickup game. They imagined themselves being the heroes of that game.

"If you are Pontoni, then you should get the Nobel Prize for that goal!" Jorge said and started down the street, dribbling the ball. Nestor had to hustle to catch up to him. Jorge looked over at him. He had that look on his face, as if he had something to say. Jorge was always a good observer and a good listener. That is what the other guys always said about him.

"Did you do your homework, Jorgito?" Nestor Carbajo asked.

"Of course," Jorge said, grinning, topping the ball with his foot, kicking it up to where Nestor had to grab it. "How about you?"

Nestor laughed. "What do you think?"

Jorge smiled. "Did you bring your books?"

"Yes," Nestor said.

"Good. Let's have a look." He walked back to the square and Nestor dogged him.

"Thanks, Jorgito," Nestor said, pointing to himself with a wink. "Pontoni will never forget you."

The friends shared a laugh and when they got back to the square, they sat down on the curb and Jorge went over the day's homework with him. The rest of the boys scattered in all directions and went home. Jorge stayed with Nestor on the curb until suppertime, and then they raced off for home, dribbling the ball back and forth between them.

CHAPTER 5

The Fan

Cardinal Bergoglio walked into his room at the Domus Internationalis Paulus VI Hotel on Via della Scrofa. The hotel, built around a 17th century stone palazzo that once housed a Jesuit college, was now an inexpensive boarding house for priests, owned by the Vatican.

Despite the chill, he threw open the window to let some fresh air into the room. He put his rollaway suitcase on the bed and looked around: single bed with nightstand.

Lamp. Radio. Small chest of drawers against one wall. Small closet cabinet. Door to even smaller bathroom.

There was a knock at the door.

He padded over to the door and opened it. It was the hotel concierge. "Your Eminence," he said. "What time would you like our car to pick you up in the morning?"

Jorge laughed. "Thank you, but I won't need a car. I will be walking to work," he said.

The Cardinal closed the door, then went over to the radio on the nightstand and switched it on, dialed through some stations, and stopped when he heard an aria.

Opera music filled the room.

He snatched up a newspaper that had been placed on his desk and paged to the sporting section. He searched the page for a long while, then closed it in frustration. He hurried over to his briefcase, pulled out his cell phone, and typed a text:

**Arrived safely in Rome. Can you tell me
the San Lorenzo score today?**

He thumbed through the contacts on his
phone until he found Father Alejandro Russo,
rector of the cathedral and one of his aides
back in Buenos Aires, and then he pushed
send. It only took a few seconds for a reply:

San Lorenzo beat River Plate, 2-0!

He smiled and wrote back:

Good! Thank you!

As he pressed "send," he remembered that
other San Lorenzo game, so long ago.

* * * *

*Jorge's father stood at the bus stop on Sunday,
December 8, 1946. "Okay, one at a time," he
said, directing traffic as his family climbed the*

stairs one by one and boarded the city bus.

"Here, Mama," Jorge said, offering her his hand. She held his sister, Marta Regina, in her other arm.

"Thank you, Jorge. You are such a gentleman," she said, boarding, shooting a proud look back at her husband.

Alberto and Oscar, Jorge's younger brothers, boarded next. Jorge looked at his father, his father nodded to him, Jorge boarded and Mario followed. After everyone was aboard, the bus roared off.

They were on their way to an away game. There is nothing more exciting than a derby: a rivalry between two neighboring teams makes the game a special occasion. But today the excitement was at a fever pitch. Today was the game that might give San Lorenzo their first championship trophy!

Caballito was the neighborhood next to Flores. It was right in the middle of the city of Buenos Aires and was home to the Ferro Carril Oeste

Football Club, better known as 'Ferro.'

The city bus roared by Gaucho's Bar and Mario swore he saw the running horse weathervane spin as they passed, the bus was going so fast. Caballito literally means 'little horse,' named because of a running horse weathervane that was mounted atop Gaucho's Bar. "You know you're in Caballito," Mario said, "when you see the weathervane."

El Templo de Madera Stadium, which hosted Ferro, was a carnival. Literally meaning, "the temple made of wood," the stadium thundered with the feet of thousands of fans, hurrying to their seats, dressed in jerseys, waving flags, and blowing horns. Entire families were going to the game today to forget the hardships of their everyday life. The soccer stadium was where everyone was part of a larger community.

Everyone came in hopes of watching a great game, of winning, and being a part of a group of people who are one in their hopes and dreams and goals. The stadium was where you could cry in joy or despair with others: where you could pray and cheer and sing your heart out. It didn't matter if you were a man, a woman, or a child, old or young.

As Jorge and his family poured into El Templo de Madera Stadium and grabbed a row of wooden seats on the visiting, San Lorenzo, side of the field, the drums beat a steady rhythm and the trumpets blared. The San Lorenzo fans and the Ferro fans, sitting on opposite sides of the field, were creating a wall of noise that covered the pitch like a cloud of anticipation full of feverish love for their teams.

The Bergoglio family sat on the San Lorenzo side because sitting anywhere else would not have been wise.

The two teams came onto the pitch for warm-ups. The host team was welcomed with deafening cheers. The San Loernzo fans booed, but their shouts were easily swallowed by the Ferro fans' thunderous cheering.

Next came the best team in the league.

Everyone in the stadium knew what was at stake.
If San Lorenzo won, they would take home the
championship trophy. But Ferro was one spot
from last place and came here to make a point.
No one, not even the best team in the league
could come to Ferro's home turf, crush them, and
leave with their trophy. If San Lorenzo wanted
to win, let it be at their own stadium. Not here.
Not today.

Jorge and every San Lorenzo fan in the stands
cheered when they saw their heroes getting ready
for the match. His eyes were glued to "The
Golden Trio:" three attacking players, fast and
furious, who looked confident and strong. They
were the legendary Pontoni; Armando Farro who
was a player known for his lethal combination
of goal scoring ability, playmaking skills, and
technique; and the unstoppable Rinaldo Martino.
The San Lorenzo fans cheered wildly. They
were thrilled at the thought of their team going
all the way. The last time San Lorenzo won a
championship was in 1933, three years before

Jorge was born. He felt he was witnessing history.

In the press stands, two sports writers for the Daily Clarin, Vicente Villanueva and Hector Villita were waiting for the game to start.

Villanueva looked at the San Lorenzo fans and scribbled in his pad, "San Lorenzo is inside the fans' hearts. For these loyal fans it is almost an obligation to come to every match to watch their team play. They know they have an unstoppable winning team, and the satisfaction is guaranteed."

His fellow writer Hector Villita felt the electricity in the air. He knew that San Lorenzo was the favorite.

Villanueva loved the team style of play. He said to Hector, "They combine old school dribbling and passing using the entire field with new school athleticism and speed. The giants of clubs like River and Boca should take notice."

"And they have the best attacking trio in the league," Villita said.

There was no argument there.

The referee whistled and San Lorenzo was immediately on the attack, led by René Pontoni. It seemed as if the entire Ferro side of the field gasped at once.

Ferro defense got the ball back but seconds later, Pontoni was on the attack again and passed to Martino. As they charged into the box, Martino took a shot and the ball sailed toward the goal. But it went high and zoomed over the crossbar. San Lorenzo fans were on their heels. Everyone screamed. It was so close, Jorge couldn't breathe.

The next 15 minutes moved fast as San Lorenzo attacked with all their might and Ferro defended and blocked the storming attacks.

Finally, at the 20th minute, Armando Farro got the ball into position and fired!

The Ferro goalkeeper almost made it but couldn't control the ball and Farro's shot slammed into the net.

San Lorenzo scored their first goal! Then, with

seconds left in the end of the first half, Pontoni
got the ball. He dribbled it between two Ferro
defenders and passed the ball to Farro, who
kicked it into the goal post. The sound of the ball
hitting the post, and the scream of joy from the
San Lorenzo fans, quickly changed to a massive
moan of disappointment, followed by a wave of
relief from the host team's fans.

The half time whistle blew.

Jorge, wearing his soccer jersey with Number
4 on it, was on his feet. His father told him that
soccer games are decided only when the last
whistle blows. He was happy. The game was
great and his team was leading one zero. But he
knew it was not enough. There were 45 minutes
left on the clock and anything could happen.

In the press box, Hector wrote in his pad that
"the San Lorenzo players were so relaxed that
they didn't seem to care whether they scored
or not. They were having so much fun out on
the field!"

* * * *

The Cardinal worked on his speech. The General Congregation of Cardinals would go on for a week, and somewhere in there, he was to deliver his speech. He loved to listen to opera and classical music while he wrote. He loved Beethoven and his favorite piece was the *Leonore Overture No. 3*.

The alarm went off exactly at 4:30am. It was a new day in Rome. In just a few hours, the 115 Cardinals who had come from all around the world would meet in the New Synod Hall in the Vatican to discuss plans for electing a new Pope. Saint Peter's Square was already starting to fill up with media and worshippers. The world was paying attention.

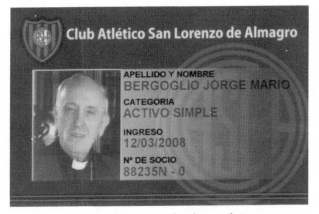

A loyal fan's membership card.

CHAPTER **6**

Two Cities

There is always a high level of secrecy involved when the College of Cardinals meets. Few people knew that ever since Pope Benedict XVI stepped aside on February 28, the Cardinals were in charge of the Church.

The Cardinal liked to take the stairs two at a time, down to the ground floor cafeteria. He remembered the steps like this when he was a boy in school; it was how he memorized the times tables, and it cracked his teacher up. Now, he just needed to make sure all was well in the lung department. He had lost most of one of his lungs to pneumonia as a young man and so as often as he could, he did these kinds of things to exercise the good one he had left.

The Cardinal planned to walk to Vatican City, as he always did. He wore the black vestments of a priest. As he waited in the cafeteria line along with other priests who resided at the Paulus VI, he marveled at the grand paintings of Biblical scenes hung around the walls of the hall. After a small breakfast, he prepared for his walk. He donned his iron pectoral cross and threw on his dark overcoat. He shoved his red cap in his coat pocket. In his coat, he kept his wallet where he had his San Lorenzo de Almagro Membership Card with his picture on it. The Club had presented it to him in 2008, after he had delivered a mass for them one Sunday. Cardinal Bergoglio was a certified fan.

His San Lorenzo de Almagro Membership Number was 8-8235.

When he got down to street level, he stepped outside and pulled his overcoat tightly around him as cold winds blew through the streets paved with cobblestones. Near the hotel, there was a lovely piazza. Although it was early morning, the streets were already crowded with people. There were tourists, families, young students, street sweepers, vendors, priests, and street performers. There were no other Cardinals staying this far into the city; they were all staying at another hotel closer to Vatican City.

He paused to watch a juggler and two lines of young students marched by, boys on one side, girls on the other, dressed alike in their school uniforms of dark skirts or pants and white shirts, all carrying books. They were followed attentively by their Sister teacher dressed in her black and white vestments as

she threaded her throng through the crowded
street, the line of children winding like a
learned snake.

"Good morning, Father," the Sister said
as she passed The Cardinal, smiling broadly
at him.

He smiled back. The sister reminded him
of his first teacher, Sister Rosa, who liked
to make an example of him every time he
daydreamed.

* * * *

*"Good morning, Jorge, how nice of you to join
us," Sister Rosa said loudly from the front of the
classroom.*

*Jorge realized he had been daydreaming. The
other students laughed. Jorge shot a quick look
over to his friend Ernesto, who rolled his eyes
in disapproval: not disapproval of daydreaming,
disapproval of Jorge getting himself caught.*

"Would you like to share your daydream with

the rest of us?" Sister Rosa challenged.

"Sorry, Sister Rosa," Jorge said, presenting his favorite teacher with one of his best smiles and shrugs. "I was just thinking about—playing ball," he said.

Sister Rosa raised an eyebrow. "Why am I not surprised? She turned and locked eyes with Ernesto. Then Nestor Carabajo. "Anyone else daydreaming about a pick-up game after school?" she asked.

No one said a word. She strolled over to Jorge's desk and stopped. "Stay awake, mister. Or you'll stay after."

It was a threat, but Jorge and Ernesto and Nestor knew she meant it. She had done it before. And every time she did it, she ruined a game for them. Ernesto and Nestor shared a look. They needed to pick up that game today. And they needed Jorge. He had the qualities of a coach. He organized the games, gave the players their positions, and had a real vision of how they should play the game. He wasn't a great player, but he understood the game, inside and out. He liked to be in defense where fierce play and a fight for every ball was left to the kids who weren't stars; the kids who did not necessarily have the natural talent to dribble, pass, and score.

After class, Jorge lingered in the schoolyard, kicking the ball around. A boy charged up and tackled him, expertly taking the ball away from him. Instead of being angry at the boy, who was several years younger than him, he smiled and said: "Good steal, Oscar!"

Oscar Bergoglio, Jorge's youngest brother, dribbled the ball away across the schoolyard, looking back, and shouting: "I'm better than you, Jorgito!"

Jorge grinned and chased after him, enjoying the challenge.

Sister Rosa came out on the schoolroom steps and watched as Jorge and his younger brother raced across the schoolyard. She knew they were going to the square to pick up their game where they left off. Jorge was so bright and had such

*great potential. But at the moment, all he had on
his mind was playing ball with his best friends.*

The temperature dropped slightly as The
Cardinal headed in the direction of the
Tiber River. He would cross the river over
the Ponte Sant'Angelo near the monument
to Saint Michael, then go up the main
thoroughfare to his final destination in
Vatican City.

The chill in the Roman air was the
opposite of his beloved Buenos Aires, which,
when he left just a day ago, was hot and
humid.

* * * *

*It was a hot day in the summer of 1946
in Buenos Aires when Jorge made his way to
Grandma Rosa's house.*

*Grandma Rosa lived only a couple of blocks
away from Membrillar Street. Jorge hurried up*

the main boulevard where he could pass the many
shops and enjoy looking in the shop windows.
He slowed as he passed the Argentine Mercado,
with the smell of roasted meat drifting out to the
street. "Buenos días, Jorgito!" the shop owner
said as he passed.

Jorge moved on and stared into the window
of the Jewish deli with its fresh baked babka and
just-cooked brisket still bubbling under the hot
lights. The Italian bakery and market smelled
of sweet oregano, tomatoes, seafood, and pasta
cooking in huge pots. He passed his dentist's
office, Doctor Delaport, whose son, Osvaldo,
played soccer with him. Jorge held his breath.
The sterile smell of a dentist's office was not
going to ruin it for the rest of the walk. He finally
let out his breath when he was beyond the dentist
and breathed deep when he got to the Armenian
restaurant as it blasted him with the exotic smells
of eggplant and yogurt and meat and green bean
dzhash with mint leaves.

As Jorge walked, the smells of the foods of so

many peoples from countries all over the world engulfed him; people who had come to Argentina to build a new life for themselves and a new home for their families. On one short block in Flores, Jorge could linger at each door that opened into a different and exciting world and culture. Here, everyone spoke the same language, but they all had another language they also spoke, a language of their ancestors.

Everyone was unique, and yet the same. His grandma, Rosa, was a perfect example: she was Italian and Argentinian and for her, it felt natural to have both cultures all wrapped up in the same person. His father, Mario, on the other hand, preferred not to speak Italian with Jorge. He wanted his children to be 100% Argentinian. But Jorge was a curious boy and wanted to know what his grandma and grandpa were talking about. He liked the sound of the Italian language as much as he loved the food.

Jorge always went to Grandma Rosa's home, a few blocks from his own, after school or after a

game until his father came home from working at
the railroad as an accountant and picked him up.
His mother was too busy with his brothers and
sister, so Grandma Rosa always had him come
over to her house. She wanted to keep her eye on
him. She wanted to watch him and give him, she
thought, the kind of education he could not get
at public school. The first thing she did was teach
him Italian, her native language. The other was
to teach him about God.

Jorge sat across from his Grandma Rosa at
her dining room table. Grandma Rosa set a glass
down in front of her young grandson Jorge and
filled it with milk from a pitcher. She had a book
opened in front of her. "What did I just give
you?" she asked him in Spanish.

"Leche," Jorge answered in Spanish.

"Wrong!" Grandma Rosa scolded. "Dimmi in
italiano," she said. "Tell me in Italian!"

"Mi scusi, Nonna," Jorge said, embarrassed.
He picked up the glass of milk and drank it all
down, then held the empty glass out to her: "Più

latte, per favore," he said. "More milk, please,"
he said in Italian.

Grandma Rosa beamed. She picked up the
pitcher of milk and poured him another glass.
"Eccellente!" she said with a smile, then reached
across the table, took his face in her hands, and
kissed his forehead.

"What was it like back in Italy, Nonna?"
Jorge asked.

Grandma Rosa sighed. "Life under the dictator
Mussolini was harsh. Business was good until
that Fascist took over. Look, Italy is one of the
most beautiful countries in the world. I love my
country. But the times were tough. People lost
their freedom and we had a hard time making
ends meet," she said. "Your father wanted more
out of life and he saw no future in Italy. Back
then, a lot of young people were looking for a
better life in America: new opportunities, a
dream of making more money and of living a
better life."

"I want to practice my Italian with Papa, but

he won't speak anything but Spanish," Jorge said, sipping some more milk. "Why?" he asked.

"He is stubborn," Grandma Rosa said. "He wants to forget about the past. He wants it to go away. But this is impossible," she continued. "If he won't remember it, then it will be up to you."

"Papa worries so much about us," Jorge said.

"Your papa is a good man. He takes good care of you," she said. "He works hard."

"He takes me to every soccer match," Jorge said.

Grandma Rosa smiled softly at Jorge. "He loves that game as much as you do," she said and added: "This is something he learned in Italy."

"I play every day, you know. We have games in the square. We all meet there, all the kids from the neighborhood and my friends from school," Jorge said.

"Are you any good?" she asked.

"We win sometimes. Oscar and Alberto are on my team, and Ernesto and Nestor," Jorge said. "Also Nathan and the dentist's son—Osvaldo.

We make a great team. Did you play soccer too,
Nonna?" he asked.

She laughed. "No. But mark my word. One
day girls will play the game, just like the
boys do."

"Can I tell you a secret, Nonna?"

"My lips are sealed," Grandma Rosa said,
running her finger over her lips.

"Sometimes I pray that we win."

"And does it work?" Grandma Rosa asked.

"Sometimes," Jorge said.

Grandma Rosa flashed a smile.

CHAPTER 7

Cooking Lessons

Not far away from Ponte Sant'Angelo, the bridge over the Tiber that led to the Vatican, The Cardinal could see the Great Synagogue of Rome on Lungotevere Dè Cenci. The building had classical architecture with Roman columns and grand mahogany doors that were 10 feet tall. The Cardinal had formed a close relationship with his dear friend, Rabbi Abraham Skorka, back in Buenos Aires, with whom he had cowritten a book and also did

a series of television shows. Back in 2007,
during Rosh Hashanah, The Cardinal visited
the synagogue in Buenos Aires to speak to the
Jewish community about honesty. He went
there to stand with them as brothers. He went
because it was true to his own heart and the
truth was always the best choice.

* * * *

*"Jorgito! The ball!" Osvaldo shouted, waving
his arms in the air.*

*Jorge saw him, passed a player, then kicked the
ball as hard as he could and watched it sail over
Osvaldo's head and straight through the window
of the house behind him, shattering it. Everyone
on both teams froze in terror as shards of glass
rained down. Then in an instant, every boy ran
in a different direction at once.*

Everyone except Jorge.

*The owner charged out of the house, holding
the ball, covered in glass, and looked up the street*

*in one direction and down in the other. Then
he looked directly in front of him and there was
Jorge standing there. "Sorry, sir," Jorge said.
"I did it."*

*The owner looked behind him at his broken
window, then back to Jorge. "You did this?"*

"I did, sir," Jorge answered.

*The owner was surprised at his answer. "Why
didn't you run like a scared rabbit like the rest of
the boys?"*

*"If I ran, then you would never know who
did it." Jorge shrugged. "But I would. And I've
already been to confession once this week."*

*The man burst out laughing. "A kid with a
conscience! Don't worry about it," he said and
handed him the ball.*

* * * *

When The Cardinal reached Lungotevere
Tor di Nona, the thoroughfare that ran
adjacent to the Tiber, he also saw the river,

which wound through the Seven Hills of
Rome like a snake. As he walked along,
he listened to the people around him and
understood what they said, thanks to his
Grandma Rosa, who had taken the time to
teach him the language of his ancestors.

The Bridge of the Holy Angel, built in
136 AD, and adorned with the statues of ten
angels, led the way to the Castel Sant'Angelo
on the other side of the Tiber. The legend
was that in 590 AD, the Archangel Michael
appeared atop the Basilica and ended the
plague. Because of this legend, the bridge was
named the Ponte Sant'Angelo in Michael's
honor.

The water of the Tiber was like flowing
glass. His journey continued over the Bridge
of Holy Angels. He was almost to Vatican
City.

At this hour in the morning, the streets of
Rome were rapidly filling with tourists; the
coffee shops along the streets packed with

tasty panini and the aromatic smell of great coffee. The Cardinal's favorite dish was his mother's *cotoletta alla Milanese*: fried veal cutlet with vegetables, which he liked served with peeled potatoes. A ristretto was his mother's one vice: a short, strong espresso. She did not know much about politics or the world war that had ended when Jorge was 10, but she knew a good espresso. And she knew how to cook. Everyone in the Bergoglio family enjoyed her cooking. When Maria Elena, Jorge's youngest sister, was born in 1949, The Cardinal found himself facing a surprising challenge.

Jorge's father, Mario, drenched in sweat, whipped open the door to the bedroom and Jorge caught a glimpse of the midwife and two of his aunts within. His mother, Regina, was in bed, screaming, about to have her fifth child. Jorge, just 13 years old, stood perfectly still holding the pot of steaming water. His father smiled down on him, snatched the pot from him, and passed him an empty pot to refill. "Boil more water, Jorgito," Mario said, and then disappeared back inside the bedroom, slamming the door. Jorge waited for a moment, then turned on his heel and walked back down the hall with the empty pot to where his two younger brothers, Alberto and Oscar, and his sister Marta Regina, sat cowering against the wall, waiting.

It was not more than a few hours later when the cries of a newborn echoed through the Bergoglio house on Membrillar Avenue. Marta Regina ran to the front door, whipped it open, and frowned. She was expecting to see a loaf of bread. Her Papa always said, "With every baby comes a loaf of bread."

Jorge, Alberto, Oscar, and Marta Regina were all sitting around the kitchen table when Mario came in and sat down. "You have a new sister," he said matter-of-factly. "Maria Elena." Then, instead of saying any more, he poured himself some water from a pitcher and gulped it down.

Jorge had never seen him look this worn out.

"What's wrong, Papa? Is Mama okay?" Jorge asked. He could see by the look on his father's face that something was not right.

Mario looked his oldest son and managed a small smile. "Is my face that obvious, Jorgito?" he said.

"You always say the door to a person's heart is through their eyes, Papa," Jorge replied. "Your eyes look scared."

Mario studied his oldest son, then beckoned him to follow him. "Let's talk." He walked away and after a moment, Jorge got up and followed his father down the long hallway to the living room near the front door. He could hear the traffic from Membrillar Street through the big wooden door.

"Your mother and sister are resting fine," Mario whispered. "But the birth has caused some problems in your Mama's legs," he continued under his breath.

"Problems?" Jorge asked.

"They're both paralyzed," Mario said and when Jorge sucked in a breath of air in shock, he hurriedly added, "But the doctor said it is nothing permanent. She will recover in time. Just for now, she cannot walk."

Jorge sighed in relief. "Without legs, it will be difficult for her to cook. So I will do the cooking," he boldly said.

Mario smiled at his son. "You are truly a gift from God, Jorgito," he said. "All right. You do the cooking."

Jorge was proud of his offer and puffed out his chest with pride.

"What dishes do you know how to cook?" Mario asked with a twinkle in his eye.

Jorge's eyes widened. "I-I don't know how to cook anything!" he said.

Mario laughed and hugged his oldest son. "We'll think of something."

The next day, Mario carried his wife Regina into the kitchen, gently placed her on her favorite dinner table chair, and made sure she was comfortable. She had finished nursing little Maria Elena, who was sleeping soundly in their bedroom. "Thank you, Mario," Regina said. "Now bring me some potatoes and a knife and a bowl."

When class was over, Jorge charged out of the schoolroom where Ernesto and Nestor were waiting for him.

"I have to go straight home," Jorge said. "I have to cook." He told his friends why and they looked at him, puzzled.

"Do you even know how to cook?" Nestor asked.

"Sure," Jorge said. "I already know how to boil water."

His friends burst out laughing.

Then they watched as Jorge leaped down the classroom stairs and walked away in the opposite direction, going home without another word.

When Jorge came home, Regina Bergoglio was sitting in her favorite chair in the kitchen, peeling potatoes and putting them in a large bowl. "No game today?" She asked.

Jorge shook his head, set his books down, and grabbed another chair. "What are we making?"

Regina reached out a delicate hand and brushed her oldest son's cheek. "Cotoletta alla Milanese, Jorgito," she said softly.

"I'll never be able to make it like you," Jorge said.

"Don't be silly. I'll teach you. All right?"

"What if no one likes my cooking?" he asked.

"As long as no one dies, you'll be OK," she said with a smile.

Jorge nodded and Jorge's Mama said: "Good. Boil some water."

"Finally something I know how to do —," Jorge joked and went about it.

The Cardinal cooks.

CHAPTER 8

Growing Pains

Straight up Via della Conciliazione were the welcoming gates of Saint Peter's Square. Even though it was still early morning, the square was already quite crowded. It seemed to The Cardinal as if the whole world had converged on Saint Peter's Square. People from all countries, dressed in their native garb, carrying flags, were together in St. Peter's. The air rang with all the languages of the world, creating a cacophony of voices and words and ideas. And no one paid attention to the priest who made his way into the square.

Many years ago, when The Cardinal was 12, he was very much like the young kids, boys and girls, who packed St. Peter's Square today.

Jorge sat at the small table near the window that faced Membrillar Street, writing a letter. On it, he drew a house with a red roof and a white picket fence. When he was finished, he stuffed the letter in an envelope and sealed it, took a last bite of egg from his breakfast plate on the table, and waited. Seconds later, Amalia Damonte, a girl his own age who lived four doors down from them on Membrillar Street, walked by with a couple of her friends, their arms loaded with school books. Jorge took a deep breath, then grabbed the letter and his own schoolbooks and charged to the front door. He kissed his mother goodbye and rocketed out of the house.

He walked swiftly up the street and caught

up with the girls when they reached the corner.
He shouldered his way between Amalia and her
girlfriend. "Hi," he said.

Amalia giggled and she and her girlfriends
shared a look and some whispering, leaving Jorge
out of the conversation, then giggled some more.
Amalia stopped walking and so did Jorge and
her girlfriends kept going. When they were a few
yards ahead of them, Amalia resumed walking
and Jorge matched her pace. "I saw you from the
window," he said, his face turning red.

Amalia smiled. "I know, I see you there every
morning, Jorgito."

"Yeah? Well, I didn't see you at the game
yesterday. You know, in the square?"

She just shrugged. "I had homework."

Jorge tried to find the right moment to give
her the letter and when they stopped at the next
corner, a block from school, he saw Ernesto and
Nestor waving at him stupidly on the other side of
the street. Desperate, he pulled the letter out of
his back pocket and shoved it at her. "This is for

you," he said, then raced across the street to join
his friends.

Amalia's girlfriends were a few yards away on
the same corner, trying to get her attention.

She was in her own world as she stood on the
corner, reading the letter, staring at a house with
the red roof and the white fence he had drawn.

The words under it said it all:

**This is where we will live
when we are married.**

Amalia gasped when she read the rest of the
letter:

**If you do not marry me,
I will join the priesthood.**

Love,

Her girlfriends surrounded her.

Jorge, Ernesto, and Nestor continued up the
street toward the school. Jorge tried to look back

to see Amalia's reaction to his letter, but Nestor turned his friend's head back to them and kicked him in the rear. "Now you're going to have to go to confession," Nestor said, and they all laughed.

The next day, Amalia did not walk past.

Nor the next.

So the day after that, Jorge waited for her; not behind his window, but right there on the street. Only her girlfriends walked by and greeted him without explanation. He was confused and he had to find out, so he stopped them on the sidewalk. "Where's Amalia?"

"We are meeting her up the street," one of her friends said, giggling.

"She's not allowed to see you anymore," another friend said.

"But—why?" Jorge asked, aching inside.

"Her father found the letter," the other friend said and both of them giggled and kept walking.

Jorge froze in his tracks and watched them go.

He never spoke with Amalia again.

But he did go to the chapel the next day. And

confessed. And in that confession, he discovered a different kind of love.

The priest told him to talk it over with his father, and Jorge did. His father, Mario, said it was because he was growing up and if he was old enough to think about girls, then he was old enough to find a job. He said work would help him understand the world, and his heart.

* * * *

His father was right about work. It gave The Cardinal perspective. He was asked many times about how he had decided to become a priest. While he was growing up, the last thing he thought he would become was a priest. If someone had told him back then that he would become a Cardinal and the Archbishop of Buenos Aires, he would have said they were crazy. Some thought he became a priest because he had a promise to keep: a promise to a young girl named

Amalia, all those years ago in a letter. But it wasn't Amalia. That was just a childish promise and he did not know what he was doing. He became a priest for a much different reason. But it also involved a girl.

When The Cardinal got to the Piazza del Santo Uffizio, he pulled his red Cardinal's cap from his dark overcoat pocket and placed it on his head. Then he removed the coat. Underneath, he wore his red and black Cardinal cassock. He folded his coat and carried it along with his black briefcase and headed past the piazza to the Papal Audience Hall of Paul VI, known as the *Sala del Sinodo*, or *Synod Hall*. This was the great hall where the College of Cardinals would begin the General Congregation and discuss the particulars of how they would run the conclave. Once the General Congregation had agreed on the rules and everyone had a chance to speak about the direction of the church, they could form a Conclave and begin the business of electing a new Pope.

Cardinal Angelo Sodano was up front, talking about security when Cardinal Bergoglio entered the hall. Sodano was the dean of the College of Cardinals and a friend. There was a wave of red and black all around the large room. Sodano informed the Cardinals that they would all have to take a vow of secrecy for the entire proceedings so that the media did not learn of what they were doing until they had decided on a Pope. There were cell phone jammers installed in the Sistine Chapel where the votes would take place and all cell phones were confiscated.

Once all 115 Cardinals were in their seats, the Congregation began the long, laborious process of administering the oath of secrecy. It took all day as Sodano called each Cardinal's name and administered the oath to them individually. After it was all over, Cardinal Bergoglio walked back to his hotel having accomplished nothing more on the first day than making a promise to keep a secret.

At this rate, it was likely that the General Congregation would not conclude and get to a real Conclave for a week.

And that is exactly what happened.

The Cardinal walks to work. He is pictured here near the Vatican as he arrives at the General Congregation.

CHAPTER 9

We Are All Equals

I t was Thursday. There had already been five General Congregations and Cardinal Bergoglio still had not been called up to deliver his speech. Then he heard Cardinal Angelo Sodano call his name. He quickly glanced at his notes. He had written them in Spanish. He walked patiently to the front and took his place behind the podium. Although he did not see himself as a candidate for the job of Pope, he had instincts that were not only forged on the streets of Buenos Aires, they were learned on the soccer pitch.

* * * *

Back in 1946, the cheering San Lorenzo fans were on their feet when the second half of the championship match began. The stadium at El Templo de Madera was sold out and no one left their seats, looking forward to what might be a glorious season finale — or a sour disappointment to the best club in the league.

Marta Regina was fast asleep in Mama's arms and slept for exactly 11 minutes. In the 56th minute, she was startled awake when Angel Zubieta shot the ball across the penalty area and Pontoni headed it in at an angle that left the goalkeeper helpless.

Ferro didn't waste any time and started a concentrated push. At the 78th minute, Piovano volleyed the ball to the goal area. Ferro's Cachiero intercepted it and kicked it in a swift move into the net.

San Lorenzo 2, Ferro 1.

The Ferro fans went ballistic.

This is how it always goes. The superior team attacks and controls and shoots… and misses. And the other team only needs one attack to score.

Everyone in the stadium knew there was enough time on the clock for the game to go either way or to end up a tie. The late goal instilled life in Ferro's players. The fans chanted and cheered. The drummers beat harder and the horns blew non stop.

"Give us another one. Give us two!" the Ferro fans chanted.

The San Lorenzo fans got over their moment of confusion. They were the best team in the league. They had the players who could make it happen. Twelve minutes away from the final whistle plus a couple of extra minutes for injury time, and 2 to 1 will be good enough. But the San Lorenzo players on the pitch didn't think about defending the score. Not for a moment. They were an attacking team and they weren't here to play out the game by running out the clock. It was risky, but this is what made them a great team.

Jorge looked at his father. He was so tense he could hear his own heart beating in his chest. His father gave him a reassuring smile that said, "We can do it. We will do it." But to be truthful, Jorge knew even his father was biting his nails.

The clock ticked by and time moved slowly. At the 85 minute mark, the San Lorenzo fans couldn't stand it anymore. A large group from the front rows poured onto the field waving flags, becoming a part of the game, uniting with their beloved players.

The referee stopped the match for a few minutes and the fans returned to the stands. But as soon as play resumed, they stormed onto the pitch again. The San Lorenzo players just stood there, grinning and taking the opportunity to drink some water. The 90th minute passed. But the game did not end. The fans cleared the pitch again.

The referee added five minutes of extra time.

At 93 minutes into the game, with only two minutes to go, Jorge shouted something at the Ferro players closest to him on the field and his mother reached over and covered his mouth. She shook her head and Jorge looked away, embarrassed.

A feeling of victory was sinking in. San Lorenzo wins 2-1 and takes home the trophy.

But just as quick as that mood swept through the San Lorenzo stands, another attack was under way and Jorge was once more on his feet.

To everyone's surprise, Silva charged into the box and fired the ball into the net!

GOAL!!

3 to 1 San Lorenzo with two minutes to play! The stands went nuts, the joy infinite.

The San Lorenzo fans didn't wait for the whistle and again streamed out onto the field. This time, the referee gave up. He blew the whistle, ending the match.

Thousands of scarves and hats flew into the air.

Hector Villita, the journalist, scribbled frantically. "It was like the hands of the champion team ignited the hearts of the fans and they were like sparks, seeking the sky," he wrote.

An ocean of fans thundered out of the San Lorenzo stands and poured onto the field, including Jorge and his father and his brothers and sisters. Mama stayed behind with the baby. Everyone hugged each other and jumped up and down for joy.

Hector Villita wrote, "I see the exhausted players crying. The fans are like a human ocean storming onto the field. They are celebrating in a way that thrills and touches everyone, including the fans of Ferro and us, the cold and cynical sports writers who saw it all."

The fans were lifting the players up into the air. No one could escape the explosion of happiness.

Jorge was witness to a moment that would forever be engraved in his heart. It was truly a glorious day.

The Clarin's headline on Monday, October 21, 1946 said it all:

SAN LORENZO MARKS A NEW EVOLUTION IN ARGENTINA'S SOCCER

After winning the title, San Lorenzo went on a tour of Spain and Portugal, one of the highlights of the club's history. After losing to Real Madrid, they went on to defeat Barcelona and both the Spanish and Portuguese national teams. The Spanish press pronounced San Lorenzo "the best team in the world." It was the best year in Jorge's life and the best year for San Lorenzo.

* * * *

Cardinal Bergoglio smiled to himself as he stood at the podium about to deliver his intervention speech to the College of Cardinals. He thought about Pontoni, the

great striker of his beloved Crows, his father
Mario refusing to speak Italian because of
his disdain for Mussolini, his Grandma Rosa
teaching him Italian for so many years as a
boy because of her love for her heritage. He
thought about his Italian roots. His love of
Rome and Italy and the beauty of the Italian
language. And so, he changed his mind.

And instead of delivering his speech in
Spanish, he delivered it in Italian.

Cardinal Bergoglio's speech was simple and
direct, and moved everyone in the room. He
told his fellow Cardinals that the Church had
to open its doors and get out in the world.
It was exactly what the College of Cardinals
wanted to hear.

When The Cardinal came to Rome, he
was convinced there was no chance he would
be elected Pope. But his speech changed the
course of history. Again, he heard the words
of his father: *Want to make God laugh?*
Make plans.

The rains came to Rome as they often do
in March and Cardinal Bergoglio couldn't
sleep. Instead of returning to his hotel room
in the center of the city, he stayed in a room
at the new Domus Sanctae Marthae residence
hall, which was next to Saint Peter's Basilica
in the Vatican. He preferred his simple room
at the Paulus VI but he could not refuse
the room at the Sanctae Marthae. All the
Cardinals were to be in one place for the
conclave. In the past, when a pope was not
chosen and the voting continued, the College
of Cardinals was locked away as prisoners
in the Sistine Chapel until they came to
a decision. Today, it is more civilized. The
Cardinals voluntarily live in the Sanctae
Marthae as equals.

The rain pounded on the roof and
Cardinal Bergoglio stared at the ceiling and
remembered the rainy season of 1998 when
he went to the slums of Villa 21-24 in Buenos
Aires to check on his work there.

* * * *

*Archbishop Jorge Bergoglio sat in a middle
seat on the Buenos Aires city bus, dressed in
the simple black vestments of a priest. Even
back then, he did not want to draw attention to
himself. If everyone around him knew he was
Archbishop, they would surround him. He was
on a mission. He watched the stops carefully
and when he saw that Villa 21-24 was the next
stop, he pulled the cord, letting the driver know
he wanted to get off. He stood, stepped up to the
front door, and looked out at Villa 21-24.*

*Outside were the streets of one of the most
dangerous barrios in Buenos Aires: Villa 21-24.
Located on the outskirts of Buenos Aires, this
neighborhood is where poor and hungry outsiders
come to the big city to look for work and to find
a roof over their heads. Only a handful of priests
volunteer to go in. The residents call them curas
villeros. Slum priests. Jorge is one of them. Villa
21-24. Hidden from the eyes and the soul of the*

people of Buenos Aires, but not from the heart and soul of Jorge. These kinds of slums exist in every city and are full of forgotten people.

But it was impossible for Jorge to forget the poor. He was a Jesuit—a student of St. Francis of Assisi. He could not look into their eyes without looking into their souls. Just as St. Francis, the son of a wealthy merchant, lived among the poor, Jorge had to be among them if he was to serve God.

The doors of the bus whooshed open.

People wondered how he could go to the most dangerous neighborhood in Buenos Aires, to which he said: "Of course I do. We are all equals in the eyes of the Lord. I'll be fine. Thank you for your concern."

He walked through mud and muck up Zavaleta Avenue. He knew the mud would be there because of the rain the night before.

When he passed the Virgin of Caacupé chapel, some children came out to greet him and he reached into his coat and pulled out wrapped sandwiches he had made for them the night before. There was enough for all of them. He knew there were always hungry children in the chapel and the children always knew their padre, Bergoglio, would have something for them to eat. Father Pepe di Paolo came out, grinning ear to ear. "Jorgito," he said and hugged his friend. "So happy you are here."

"Hello, Father Pepe, what's going on down at the pitch?"

Pepe winked. "See for yourself!"

The Cardinal and Father Pepe walked side-by-side down the street and when they reached the soccer field at the end of the road, The Cardinal's face lit up. A pick-up game was in full swing.

The Cardinal recognized most of the players as former drug addicts he had worked with before. He turned to Pepe and said, "You never know who is the next Pontoni, if given half a chance."

He and Father Pepe walked back to the chapel. When they got there, Jorge scraped the mud from his shoes and entered. A carpentry class full of

men in their early 20s was in one of the Sunday
school classrooms. He stuck his head in and
lingered for a moment. Another priest was up
front demonstrating how to set a mitered angle on
a two-by-four. The priest waved back, happy to
see him.

"We would not have this class without you.
Thank you for collecting the money to feed the
people and start this carpentry class, Padre,"
Father Pepe said.

"These men were thrown away because of
their addictions. If they're old enough to score
drugs, they're old enough to learn a trade," The
Cardinal said.

The medical clinic was next door and the beds
were full. "Padre, it is so good to see you, I am
so happy you came," the Sister said.

"Thank you for inviting me, Sister," The
Cardinal said as he was led into the windowless
room full of beds with sick men in them. He
moved to the first bed and took the hand of a
man lying there, slack-jawed and unshaven.

"God be with you, my son," Jorge whispered and the man's eyes filled with tears. "May I wash your feet?"

The man blinked away a tear and nodded.

Black or white smoke?
The ovens in the Sistine Chapel.

CHAPTER 10

Two Confessions

Saint Peter's Square was wet from the heavy rains the night before. Over 200,000 people from all around the world had camped out in the square and its environs. From the air, it was nothing but a sea of colorful umbrellas spreading like a rainbow wave from the Vatican through the streets of Rome to the Coliseum. Camera platforms were everywhere and giant flat screen monitors dotted the landscape like billboards, ready to display the theatrical drama to the world. No one in the streets of Rome who was even remotely close was going to move until the church announced a Pontiff. They came to witness history. They wanted to see some white smoke.

The floor echoed in the Sistine Chapel as the Cardinals filed in to begin the papal conclave.

The Cardinal walked through the Sistine alongside his friend, Cardinal Claudio Hummes from Brazil, in a two-line procession. All the Cardinals chanted prayers as they walked, but they were drowned out by workers getting the stoves ready where the ballots from each round of voting would be burned. The twin stoves were cast iron and first used in 1939. Copper piping ran to both stoves and the piping, secured by steel scaffolding, reached up all the way to the ceiling and out the roof to the rooftop chimney. One of the cast iron stoves was for the burning of the ballots and the other was an auxiliary fumigating oven next to it where special chemicals were added to turn smoke black or white.

If black smoke comes out of the Sistine Chapel chimney, all the people in St. Peter's Square will know that no Pope has been chosen. If the smoke is white, however, they will know they have a new Pope.

As the Cardinals walked, the artwork of Botticelli, Rosselli, and Signorelli watched over them from all sides. The Sistine Chapel ceiling is covered with the amazing paintings of the magnificent Michelangelo Buonarroti.

Out in the square, there were no borders or boundaries, nor closed doors. All eyes were on the chimney that jutted from the roof of the conclave room in the Sistine Chapel.

Cardinal Bergoglio sat next to Hummes. Half the Cardinals were on one side of the room, half on the other, facing each other. The room was pin-drop quiet as the Cardinals scrawled on their ballot papers. When they finished, the Cardinals dropped their folded ballot papers into the urn that rested on the altar. On the wall, above the urn, was Jesus Christ looking back at them from Michelangelo's painting, *The Last Judgment*.

When all the votes were cast, the senior cardinal, Giovanni Battista Re, and two others, counted the ballots as Battista Re read the names aloud. A candidate needed two-thirds plus one for a total of 77 votes in order for the white smoke to billow out from the Sistine Chapel chimney.

In the end, no one received enough votes. The ballot counters delivered the ballots to the stove to be burned and added chemicals to the auxiliary stove to create black smoke. The Cardinal scurried along the walkway back to the Sanctae Marthae, and plopped down in the chair in the confessional reserved only for Cardinals. A priest was already there waiting for him.

"Bless me, Father, for I have sinned," he

said softly, then continued.

There was another confession the Cardinal made; one that changed his life when he was 17.

* * * *

"Hurry up, Jorgito!" Ernesto shouted. He was standing on the sidewalk on Membrillar Street in front of Jorge's house with Nestor and a couple of girls. The boys had picnic baskets weighted down with food. It was September 21, 1953, the first day of spring. When 17-year-old Jorge came out the front door, the girl with long dark hair lit up when she saw him. She really liked him. Jorge saw the girl and flashed a smile. She reached out her hand and he took it and the group walked briskly up the street toward the hall a few blocks up, where they were all going dancing.

When they passed a restaurant, Jorge noticed a wealthy man in an expensive suit sitting at an outdoor table, eating, while a group of children in dirty clothes watched with hungry eyes. Jorge looked at his friends in dismay, but did not say anything. He lingered for a moment, but could not decide what to do about what he was seeing. He felt bad for the children. He himself had never known hunger, but he could see it in their eyes. They passed a chapel on the next corner.

The dance hall was just a few blocks away and soon they would all be doing the tango to the latest Argentinian tunes. But when they finally arrived, Jorge hung back. "Come on, Jorgito!" the girl said. "Let's dance!" She laughed and hurried into the hall. Jorge looked inside. The girl beckoned him to come in. Instead, he backed up a step. "I'll be right back," he shouted over the music. He turned and walked away.

"Jorgito! Where are you going?" Nestor shouted after him.

Jorge said, "I don't know," and kept on walking back towards the chapel. It was where Jorge and his family attended mass every Sunday and Jorge knew his way around. A priest with his

back to him was kneeling at the altar when Jorge
stepped in. "Father?" Jorge asked.

The priest turned around and Jorge did not
recognize him. "Oh, I'm sorry, I-I thought you
were someone else."

The priest smiled. "I'm new," he said. "Can I
help you?"

Jorge shifted uncomfortably from one foot to
the other. Finally, he said: "I'm not sure, Father.
May I take confession?" he asked.

The priest smiled. "Of course, my son."

Jorge entered the booth and sat down. "I think
I came looking for God, Father," he said.

"Well, he beat you to it," the priest said,
chuckling. "He has been waiting for you."

When Jorge stepped out of that confessional
in Flores, he never went back to the community
center, nor did he ever see that girl again.

That night, Jorge's mother sat in her chair and
his father stood behind it as Jorge told them what
had happened to him: "You see, I realized he was
waiting for me. I was looking for him, but he

found me first," Jorge said. "I've never said this before, but I think I want to give my life to God. I want to become a priest."

His father, Mario, was all smiles, "This is wonderful news, Jorge," he said.

Regina burst into tears.

"Why are you crying, Mama?" Jorge asked, taking her hand. "Are you not happy for me?"

"No!" she said, teary-eyed. "I was hoping you would become a doctor!"

CHAPTER 11

I Accept

When a Papal Conclave does not elect a Pope on the first ballot on the first day, then on each subsequent day, there are four more votes—two each morning and two each afternoon—until one is chosen. Cardinal Giovanni Battista Re read Cardinal Bergoglio's name more than 70 times. The Cardinal shifted uncomfortably, realizing there was a distinct possibility he would not be heading back to his beloved Buenos Aires any time soon. It had been quite a long time since he knew he would never be a soccer player or a doctor. But becoming Pope—that was not something he could decide. His calling, which began almost fifty years ago in a confessional, led him to become a Cardinal. Now, in a matter of minutes, it might make him the head of the Catholic Church.

"Don't forget the poor," Cardinal Claudio Hummes whispered to him, hugging him.

"I won't, dear Claudio," Jorge whispered back. He looked down at his hand. It was shaking. When he looked up, his eyes met Claudio's. "But that was only 70 votes." He grinned at his friend. "I'm still off the hook."

"Not for long," Claudio said and winked.

In the history of the Conclave that began in 1276, the College of Cardinals had never elected a non-European Pope, let alone a Jesuit. This fact did not escape The Cardinal as he listened to Cardinal Giovanni Battista Re read his name for the 77th time. The

Sistine Chapel erupted in applause and before he could even think, The Cardinal was on his feet and heard the words come out of his mouth: "Accetto," he said in Italian. "I accept."

"I choose the name Francis in honor of Saint Francis of Assisi," he said and the Sistine Chapel exploded in applause once more. Saint Francis of Assisi, Francisco in Italian, was not only the son of a wealthy merchant who dedicated his life to the poor, he was the patron saint of Italy. Francisco was also the name of Cardinal Bergoglio's great grandfather.

And so, in the late afternoon of March 13, 2013, on the fifth vote, Cardinal Jorge Mario Bergoglio was elected Pope.

The ballots burned bright in the Sistine Chapel stove, and white smoke billowed from the chimney for the world to see. The hundreds of thousands of devotees who spent days camped out around Vatican City erupted in cheering and applause.

As the Papal aides escorted the newly elected Pope to fit him for the Papal cassock, Cardinal Hummes tagged alongside his friend.

"God help you for what you have done," Jorge whispered to his friend as they marched toward the fitting room.

A few minutes later, in the fitting room, the Papal tailor brought in the elaborate fur-lined, jewel-encrusted, white Papal cassock that Pope Benedict XVI once wore, along with an elaborate golden Pectoral cross and fancy red shoes made by Italian fashion designer Prada.

"We have three sizes of cassocks, your Eminence: small, medium, and large," the first tailor said.

"I won't need those," Jorge said. "I will wear the simple white cassock—and this," he said, pulling his iron pectoral cross from his briefcase. "And of course, these—my old friends," he said, pointing down to his feet, showing the tailor that he was wearing his favorite black oxfords.

Twenty minutes later, the tailor returned with the austere white cassock, tailored to fit the new Pope. Jorge removed the scarlet and black Cardinal vestments and the tailor immediately saw the long jagged scar on his chest running from his breastplate to the middle of his back.

Jorge put on the plain white Papal cassock and his iron pectoral cross. "When I was 21, I had a terrible case of pneumonia," he explained. "It was 1957 and I had not yet committed to joining the seminary."

* * * *

Jorge's bed was soaked with his sweat when his father rushed into the room. He took the thermometer from his 21-year-old son's mouth, looked at it, and frowned. Jorge was delirious and probably did not know where he was. Regina came into the room, clutching a dishtowel, sobbing. "The doctor is here, Mario," she said between sobs. The doctor politely pushed past Regina and took one look at Jorge, then turned to Mario and said, "I cannot help him here. We must bring him to the hospital."

When Jorge woke up, he was in a hospital bed and he had no idea how he had gotten there. He had tubes running from his arm and his nose and when he looked down, he saw his chest wrapped in gauze bandages and surgical tape. It hurt a lot. The last thing he remembered was the fever dreams and now he no longer felt ill. Just sore. Someone was holding his hand. His mother.

His father was speaking in hushed tones with a man in a white lab coat and his Nonna Rosa appeared next to his mother. He could not speak because there was a tube down his throat. He felt some pain, and then the doctor came over and turned a valve on his IV, and he drifted off to sleep.

The Cardinal patted his scar under
his cassock. "Back then, there were no
antibiotics. Not in Argentina, anyway. So to
save my life, the doctors removed most of this
lung," he said, patting his side.

The tailor nodded. "We are all glad he did,
your Eminence," he said and left.

Fifty years had passed since the operation
and now at age 76, The Cardinal was as fit
as can be. As he prepared to greet his new
worldwide congregation, he reached into his
briefcase, took a yellowed envelope from his
breviary, and tucked it away into his cassock.
The envelope contained words of wisdom
that he knew he would need to read again
very soon.

CHAPTER 12

One Pope

Pope Francis hurried straight through the Sala Regia to the Capella Paolina and asked to be alone for a few minutes. On the other side of the Capella Paolina was another room and beyond that, the famous balcony where he would be introduced to the world in just a few minutes. He could hear the sounds of the many thousands of people who were waiting excitedly outside. He felt great anxiety. To make it go away, he closed his eyes and tried to relax, and made every thought disappear, even the thought of refusing to accept the position as Pope. At a certain point, he was filled with a great light. It lasted a moment, but to him it seemed a very long time. Then the light faded. He got up quickly and walked into the room where the Cardinals were waiting.

In his cassock he kept his breviary and in that breviary was a yellow envelope with a letter in it from his Grandma Rosa. She had written it to him when he left for the seminary in 1958. It was the last thing she had ever written to him and he had kept it with him all these years in his book of prayers. It was a simple letter from her to her grandchildren, and it read:

> *May my grandchildren, to whom I have given the best of my heart, have a long and happy life. But if there are days of pain or illness, or if the loss of a loved one fills them with despair, may they remember that a*

whisper of a prayer and a look to Mary at the feet of the cross, can be like a drop of balm on even the deepest and most painful wounds.

Cardinal Camerlengo, the chief officer of the Apostolic Camera, the Financial Council of the Pope, was waiting for him near a table. Spread out on the table was a large parchment that all elected Popes must sign if they accept the position.

Pope Francis walked silently up to the paper and signed it. When he was finished, he handed the pen to Cardinal Camerlengo who countersigned it.

They were in the Room of Tears. It led to the Central Loggia, where Pope Francis would meet the world. The Room of Tears, where all Popes began their journey, was the room where the Popes that came before him realized the weight that they had accepted on their shoulders in God's name. Many of them cried, which was why it was called The Room of Tears.

Pope Francis was cheerful. He was about to open the doors of the church to the world. He was the first Jesuit Pope. He was the first Pope from the Americas. He had one foot in the Old World, and one in the new. From Portacomaro, Italy, to Flores, Buenos Aires, Argentina: two worlds, but one Pope.

Pope Francis knew that Ernesto and Nestor, and his youngest sister, Maria Elena, were back home watching on television and that although his beloved *Los Cuervos de Boedo* would not win every game—even if he was the Pope—they won the last one and that's how you win them, one at a time.

Pope Francis joined Georg Gänswein, Prefect of the Papal Household, and Cardinal Tauran, the President of the Pontifical Council, at the entryway that led to the Central Loggia. Each of them stood at a red velvet curtain, left and right, waiting for him.

"Ready, your Eminence?" Cardinal Tauran asked.

Jorge closed his eyes, and nodded.

That was the signal. The two Cardinals pulled the curtains apart and Cardinal Tauran marched out to the microphone on the Central Loggia.

The crowd exploded in cheers and applause, and then grew silent in the next heartbeat.

Cardinal Tauran leaned into the microphone: "*Habemus Papam!*" he shouted to the world. "We have a Pope!"

Jorge straightened the simple iron pectoral cross on his chest, then stepped solemnly out on the Central Loggia and met the world for the first time, as Pope Francis. He already knew how he would end his speech:

"Pray for me!"

*First introduction to the public of the
newly elected Pope Francis.*

Epilogue

ON THE DAY Cardinal Jorge Bergoglio was elected Pope, Argentina held its National Lottery. The winning number was 8235. Someone commented that it was quite a coincidence considering Pope Francis's San Lorenzo de Almagro Membership Number was 8-8235.

Someone else reminded them what Albert Einstein said:

"Coincidences are God's way of remaining anonymous."

*A San Lorenzo commemorative jersey
honoring Pope Francis.*

*The Cardinal showing the jersey of his
beloved team.*

Acknowledgements

The writer wishes to thank Yitzhak Ginsberg, who made it happen and kept me honest.

Diego Melamed's time machine went where no man had gone before.

And Michele Caterina made it all make sense.

The publisher wishes to thank Yosi Ohayon, Taly Ginsberg, Lynn Snyder, and everyone at Sole Books who contributed to this book.

You all have our undying gratitude.

Works Cited

"1946 Argentine Primera División." *Wikipedia.* Wikimedia Foundation, 20 Aug. 2013. Web. 27 Aug. 2013.

Alpert, Emily. "Neighbors, Old Friends Offer Up Stories of Pope Francis as a Boy." *Los Angeles Times,* 15 Mar. 2013. Web. 27 Aug. 2013.

Alsop, Harry. "Pope Francis: 20 Things You Didn't Know." *The Telegraph,* 14 Mar. 2013. Web. 27 Aug. 2013.

Bennett-Smith, Meredith. "Amalia Damonte, Pope Francis' Childhood Sweetheart, Rejected Young Man's Marriage Proposal (VIDEO)." *The Huffington Post,* 15 Mar. 2013. Web. 27 Aug. 2013.

Bensinger, Ken. "Pope Francis, Soccer Fan, Scores with Argentina Media." *Los Angeles Times,* 14 Mar. 2013. Web. 27 Aug. 2013.

Bergoglio, Jorge Mario. *On Heaven and Earth: Pope Francis on Faith, Family, and the Church in the Twenty-first Century.* Boston, MA: Doubleday, 2013. Print.

Bergsma, John. "Pope Francis' Actual Football Club Card." *The Sacred Page,* 14 Mar. 2013. Web. 27 Aug. 2013.

Burgess, Tina. "Pope: One Lung and 9 More Less-Known, Unusual Facts about Pope Francis." *Examiner.com,* 14 Mar. 2013. Web. 27 Aug. 2013.

"Campeon, Por Santo Y... Por Bueno." *Clarin* [Buenos Aires], 9 Dec. 1946, Sports (cover) sec.: n. pag. Print.

Ciancio, Antonella. "Pope Francis Feted in Italian
        Ancestral Village." *Reuters*, 15 Mar. 2013. Web.
        27 Aug. 2013.

Connor, Tracy. "Pope Stuns Newsstand Owner by Calling
        to Cancel Home Delivery." *NBC News*, 22 Mar.
        2013. Web. 27 Aug. 2013.

Cullinane, Susannah. "Pope Benedict XVI's Resignation
        Explained." *Cable News Network*, 28 Feb. 2013.
        Web. 27 Aug. 2013.

Di Stefano, "Humble May Have Played with Pope"
        Deccan Herald. Reuters, 18 Mar. 2013. Web.
        27 Aug. 2013.

Domus Internationalis Paulus VI - Informazioni, n.d.
        Web. 27 Aug. 2013.

"El Papa Saluda a "los Cuervos," Los Hinchas Del San
        Lorenzo De Almagro." *YouTube*, 10 Apr. 2013. Web.
        27 Aug. 2013.

Escobar, Mario. *Francis: Man of Prayer*. Nashville, TN:
        Thomas Nelson, 2013. Print.

"Estadio Pedro Bidegain." *Wikipedia*. Wikimedia
        Foundation, 31 July 2013. Web. 27 Aug. 2013.

Fausset, Richard. "Pope Francis' Latin American
        Upbringing Is Unique among Popes." *DeseretNews.
        com*. Los Angeles Times, 23 Mar. 2013. Web.
        27 Aug. 2013.

France-Presse, Agence. "Pope Francis Remembered as
        a 'Little Devil' at School." *GlobalPost*. Agence
        France-Presse, 14 Mar. 2013. Web. 27 Aug. 2013.

Glatz, Carol. "Pope Chooses Silver Ring, Pallium Style in
        Keeping with Predecessor." *Catholic News Service*,
        19 Mar. 2013. Web. 27 Aug. 2013.

Greenspan, Jesse. "8 Things You May Not Know About the Papal Conclave." *History.com*. A&E Television Networks, 11 Mar. 2013. Web. 27 Aug. 2013.

Guardian Staff. "Pope Francis: 13 Key Facts about the New Pontiff." *The Guardian*, 13 Mar. 2013. Web. 27 Aug. 2013.

Henao, Luis A. "Argentinians Celebrate Francis as Their 'Slum Pope'." *NBC Latino*, 15 Mar. 2013. Web. 27 Aug. 2013.

Hoffman, Matthew. "Life, Family and Culture News." *LifeSiteNews.com*. Latin American Correspondent, 18 Mar. 2013. Web. 27 Aug. 2013.

"Jubilo Que Acerca Al Pasado." *Clarin* [Buenos Aires], 9 Dec. 1946, Sports sec.: 30. Print.

Lucero, Diego. "Pontoni Marco Un Gol Como Para Pasarlo El Colon." *Clarin* [Buenos Aires], 9 Dec. 1946, Sports sec.: n. pag. Print.

Meichtry, Stacy, and Alessandra Galloni. "Fifteen Days in Rome: How the Pope Was Picked." *Wall Street Journal*, 14 Apr. 2013. Web. 27 Aug. 2013.

Memmott, Mark. "Pope Francis Is Now 'Papa Crow' to His Favorite Soccer Club." *NPR*, 14 Mar. 2013. Web. 27 Aug. 2013.

Merolla, Daniel. "Pope Francis Is Humble Son of Argentine Workman." *InterAksyon.com*. Agence France-Presse, 14 Mar. 2013. Web. 27 Aug. 2013.

Miller, Victoria. "Pope Francis Was a Devilish Little Boy According to Teacher." *Philadelphia Pop Culture Examiner.com*, 20 Mar. 2013. Web. 27 Aug. 2013.

Mojonnier, Laura. "Curas Villeros." *The Argentina Independent*, 14 Mar. 2011. Web. 27 Aug. 2013.

Peck, Brooks. "San Lorenzo Wears Pope Francis on Their Shirts for Match against Colon, Win with an Own Goal." *Yahoo! Sports*. Dirty Tackle, 16 Mar. 2013. Web. 27 Aug. 2013.

"Pope Francis and His Good Friend the Rabbi." *JerusalemOnline*, 2 July 2013. Web. 27 Aug. 2013.

"Pope Francis: His Holiness the Commuter and Football Fan." *RSS*. Euronews, 14 Mar. 2013. Web. 27 Aug. 2013.

"Pope Francis Makes Spontaneous Appearances on His First Sunday." *WLTX.com* Web Staff, 17 Mar. 2013. Web. 27 Aug. 2013.

"Pope Francis: The History Behind the Ancient Christian Ritual of Washing Feet." *The Telegraph*, 29 Mar. 2013. Web. 27 Aug. 2013.

"Pope Recalls 'that Goal by René Pontoni'" *MARCA. com (English Version)*, 13 Aug. 2013. Web. 27 Aug. 2013.

Press, Associated. "Pope Francis: Soccer Fan." *CBSNews*. CBS Interactive, 14 Mar. 2013. Web. 27 Aug. 2013.

Quijano, Elaine. "Argentines Recall Pope's Humility (and Soccer Abilities)." *CBSNews*, 15 Mar. 2013. Web. 27 Aug. 2013.

Reidy, Tim. "What Happens in the General Congregation?" *America: The National Catholic Review*, 4 Mar. 2013. Web. 27 Aug. 2013.

Rossini, Connie. "Meet Pope Francis (for Kids and Their Parents), *Contemplative Homeschool Blog*, 19 Mar. 2013. Web. 27 Aug. 2013.

Rubin, Sergio. *Pope Francis: Conversations with Jorge Bergoglio: His Life in His Own Words*. New York: Penguin Group (USA) Incorporated, 2013. Print.

Santisteban, Claudio. "Pope Francis Childhood Home in
    Flores Neighborhood of Buenos Aires." *Demotix*,
    15 Mar. 2013. Web. 27 Aug. 2013.
Scalfari, Eugenio. "The Pope: How The Church Will
    Change." *La Repubblica* [Rome] 1 Oct. 2013,
    Cultura sec.: n. pag. Print. "Sister Remembers Pope
When They Were Young." *RSS*.
    Euronews, 19 Mar. 2013. Web. 27 Aug. 2013.
"SS Principessa Mafalda." *Wikipedia*. Wikimedia
    Foundation, 24 July 2013. Web. 27 Aug. 2013.
Staff, Wire Reports And. "Pope Francis Makes Surprise
    Call to Fellow Argentines." *USA Today*, 19 Mar. 2013.
    Web. 27 Aug. 2013.
"Un Dia Como Hoy." *San Lorenzo Encyclopedia*,
    12 Aug. 2010. Web. 27 Aug. 2013.
Villita, Hector. "Entre Martino Y Pontoni Pusieron Los
    Remaches." *Clarin* [Buenos Aires], 9 Dec. 1946,
    Sports sec.: 31. Print.
Viola, Frank. "15 Interesting Facts About Francis—
    The New Pope." *Patheos*, 5 Aug. 2013.
    Web. 27 Aug. 2013.

ALSO BY MICHAEL PART
AND SOLE BOOKS

The Flea – The Amazing Story of Leo Messi

The captivating story of soccer legend
Lionel Messi, from his first touch at age five in
the streets of Rosario, Argentina, to his first
goal on the Camp Nou pitch in Barcelona,
Spain. The Flea tells the amazing story of a boy
who was born to play the beautiful game and
destined to become the world's greatest soccer
player.

MORE FROM SOLE BOOKS

The Wild Soccer Bunch Series
by Joachim Masannek

The World's Best Soccer Strikers
by Noah Davis

I Love Soccer
by Stephen Berg

Baby First Soccer
by Stephen Berg